MATHEMATICS

Fiona Mapp

Contents

HOW TO USE THIS BOOK

What we have included:

★ Those topics at Level 5 that are trickiest to get right.
★ All Level 6–7 content described by the National Curriculum descriptors.

 INTRODUCTION – This section tells you what you need to do to get to Level 6 or 7. It picks out the key learning objective and explains it simply to you.

 QUESTION – The question helps you to learn by doing. It is presented in a similar way to a SATs question and gives you a real example to work with.

 FLOW CHART – This shows you the steps to use when completing questions like this. Some of the advice appears on every flow chart (read the question then read it again). This is because this is the best way of getting good marks in the test.

 TOP TIP BOXES – These provide test hints and general tips on the topic.

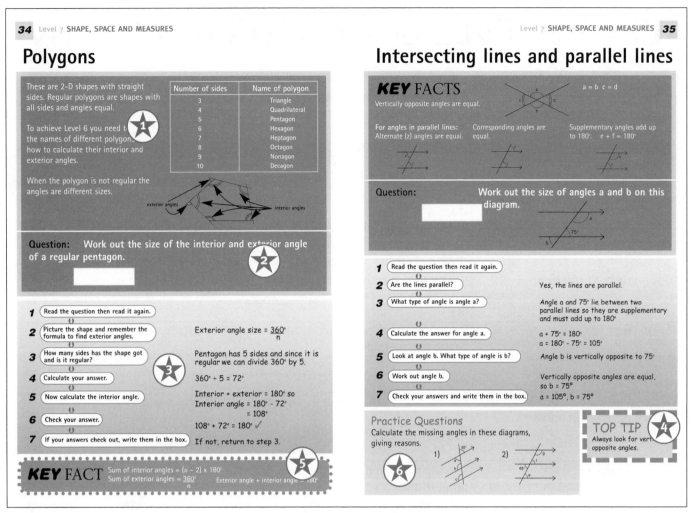

 KEY FACT – On some pages there are key facts which will give you essential information to use when revising each topic.

 PRACTICE QUESTIONS – This is where you have to do the work! Try each question using the technique in the flow chart then check your answers at the back. Practising questions is the best way to help improve your understanding.

GOOD LUCK!

ACHIEVE LEVEL 6-7 MATHS – OBJECTIVES

This chart allows you to see which objectives in the National Numeracy Strategy have been covered. We have matched the objectives directly with each page of Achieve Level 6-7 so you can monitor progress. **Text in bold denotes key objectives.**

Page no.	Title	Objective
LEVEL 5 TRICKY BITS		
6–7	Multiplication and division	Use standard column procedures to add and subtract integers and decimals of any size, including a mixture of large and small numbers.
8–9	Simple formulae	Use letter symbols to represent unknown numbers. Use simple formulae from mathematics and other subjects.
10	Units of measure	Use units of measurement to estimate, calculate and solve problems in an everyday context. Know rough metric equivalents of imperial measures in daily use.
11	Graphs	Solve a problem by extracting and interpreting data in graphs, charts and diagrams.
NUMBER, CALCULATIONS AND ALGEBRA		
12	Decimals	Order decimals.
13	One quantity as a percentage estimate of another	Express one given number as a percentage or fraction of another.
14	Adding and subtracting fractions	Add and subtract fractions by writing them with a common denominator.
15	Equivalent fractions, decimals and percentages	**Use the equivalence of fractions, decimals and percentages to compare proportions.**
16	Ratio	Interpret and use ratio in a range of contexts including solving word problems.
17	Finding the nth term of a linear sequence	**Generate sequences from practical contexts and write an expression to describe the nth term of an arithmetic sequence.**
18–19	Linear equations	**Construct and solve linear equations with integer coefficients using an appropriate method.**
20–21	Drawing linear graphs	**Plot the graphs of linear functions, where y is given explicitly in terms of x.**
22	Significant figures and estimating	Estimate calculations by rounding numbers to one significant figure and multiplying or dividing mentally.
23	Multiplying and dividing by numbers between 0 and 1	Understand the effects of multiplying and dividing by numbers between 0 and 1; use the laws of arithmetic and inverse operations.
24–25	Understanding proportional changes and repeated percentage	Solve problems involving percentage changes. **Use proportional reasoning to solve a problem, choosing the correct numbers to take as 100% or as a whole.**
26	Efficient use of a calculator	Use a calculator efficiently and appropriately to perform complex calculations with numbers of any size.
27	Finding the nth term of a quadratic sequence	Find the next term and the nth term of quadratic sequences and functions and explore their properties.
28	Multiplying out brackets	**Construct and solve linear equations with integer coefficients (with and without brackets).**
29	Solving inequalities	Solve linear inequalities in one variable.
30–31	Simultaneous equations	**Solve a pair of simultaneous linear equations by eliminating one variable; link a graphical representation of an equation or a pair of equations to the algebraic solution.**
SHAPE, SPACE AND MEASURES		
32	2-D Representations of 3-D objects	Visualise and use 2-D representations of 3-D objects; analyse 3-D shapes through 2-D projections, including plans and elevations.
33	Triangles and quadilaterals	Classify triangles and quadrilaterals by their geometric properties.

Page no.	Title	Objective
34	Polygons	Explain how to find, calculate and use the interior and exterior angles of regular polygons.
35	Intersecting lines and parallel lines	Solve problems using properties of angles including parallel and intersecting lines.
36	Logo and transformations	Transform 2-D shapes by combinations of translations, rotations and reflections, on paper and using ICT.
37	Area of plane shapes	Deduce and use formulae for the area of a triangle, parallelogram and trapezium; calculate areas of compound shapes made from rectangles and triangles.
38	The circle	Know and use the formulae for the circumference and area of a circle.
39	Volume of cubes and cuboids	Know and use the formula for the volume of a cuboid; calculate volumes and surface areas of cuboids and shapes made from cuboids.
40	Enlargement	Level 6 – Enlarge 2-D shapes, given a centre of enlargement and a whole number scale factor, on paper and using ICT.
		Level 7 – Enlarge 2-D shapes, given a fractional scale factor; recognise the similarity of the resulting shapes; understand the implications of enlargement for area and volume.
41	Loci	Find the locus of a point that moves according to a simple rule, both by reasoning and by using ICT; extend to more complex rules involving loci and simple constructions.
42–43	Pythagoras' theorem	Understand and apply Pythagoras' theorem.
44	Accuracy of measurement	Recognise that measurements given to the nearest whole unit may be inaccurate by up to one half of the unit in either direction.
45	Compound measures	Understand and use measures of speed (and other compound measures such as density or pressure) to solve problems.
46–47	Areas of compound shapes and volumes of prisms	Calculate lengths, areas and volumes in prisms, including cylinders.
HANDLING DATA		
48–49	Frequency diagrams for continuous data	Construct frequency diagrams for discrete and continuous data on paper and using ICT.
50	Pie charts	Construct pie charts for categorical data on paper and using ICT.
51	Probability	Identify all the mutually exclusive outcomes of an experiment; know that the sum of probabilities of all mutually exclusive outcomes is 1 and use this when solving problems.
52–53	Possible outcomes for combined events	Level 6 – find and record all possible mutually exclusive outcomes for single events and two successive events in a systematic way.
		Level 7 – Understand relative frequency as an estimate of probability and use this to compare outcomes of experiments.
54–55	Scatter diagrams	Select, construct and modify, on paper and using ICT, suitable graphical representation to progress an enquiry. Use scatter graphs to develop further understanding of correlation.
56–57	Averages of grouped data	Find the median and quartiles for large data sets; estimate the mean, median and interquartile range of a large set of grouped data.
58	Frequency polygons	Select, construct and modify suitable graphical representation to progress an enquiry, including frequency polygons on paper and using ICT.
59	Designing questionnaires	Design a survey or experiment to capture the necessary data from one or more sources; determine the sample size and degree of accuracy needed; design, trial and if necessary refine data collection sheets; construct tables for large discrete and continuous sets of raw data, choosing suitable class intervals; design and use two-way tables. Identify possible sources of bias and plan how to minimise it.
60–61	Relative frequency and probability	Understand relative frequency as an estimate of probability and use this to compare outcomes of experiments.

Multiplication and division

You need to be able to multiply and divide a 3-digit number by a 2-digit number without a calculator!

Question: Write in the missing number. $192 \times 49 =$ [ ]

1 (Read the question then read it again.)

$192 \times 49 = ?$

2 (Picture the numbers.)

192 is close to 200.
49 is close to 50.

3 (Study the numbers and think about them.)

192×49 is approximately
$200 \times 50 = 10000$

4 (Calculate your answer.)

$$
\begin{array}{r}
192 \\
\times \quad 49 \\
\hline
1728 \quad (192 \times 9) \\
7680 \quad (192 \times 40) \\
\hline
9408
\end{array}
$$

5 (Does your answer look sensible? If it does then write it in the box. If it doesn't then go back to Step 3.)

9408 is close to 10000 (see Step 3). Our answer looks sensible!

Question: Write in the missing number. $614 \times 29 =$ [ ]

1 (Read the question then read it again.)

$614 \times 29 =$

2 (Picture the numbers.)

614 is close to 600.
29 is close to 30.

3 (Study the numbers and think about them.)

614×29 is approximately
$600 \times 30 = 18000$

4 (Calculate your answer.)

$$
\begin{array}{r}
614 \\
\times \quad 29 \\
\hline
5526 \quad (614 \times 9) \\
12280 \quad (614 \times 20) \\
\hline
17806
\end{array}
$$

5 (Does your answer look sensible? If it does, write it in the box. If it doesn't, go back to Step 3.)

17806 is approximately 18000 (see Step 3). Our answer looks sensible!

Now let's try division.

Question: Write in the missing number. 894 ÷ 12 = [ ]

1 Read the question then read it again.

894 ÷ 12 =

2 Picture the numbers – what do they look like?

894 is close to 900.
12 is close to 10.

3 Study the numbers and think about them.

894 ÷ 12 is approximately
900 ÷ 10 = 90

4 Calculate your answer.

$$\begin{array}{r} 74.5 \\ 12{\overline{)894.0}} \\ -\underline{84} \\ 54 \\ -\underline{48} \\ 60 \\ -\underline{60} \\ 00 \end{array}$$

5 If your answer looks sensible, write it in the box.

Our answer is 74.5

KEY FACTS x and ÷ are opposites

Use this fact to help with tricky questions. For example:

21 x 16 = 336   336 ÷ 21 = 16

16 x [ ] = 336   so   336 ÷ 16 = 21   Our missing number is 21.

TOP TIP 2

Be neat. Keep your numbers in the right columns.

WRONG ✗
```
    312
x    14
   3120
   1248
   4368
```

RIGHT ✓
```
    312
x    14
   3120
   1248
   4368
```

★ TOP TIP 1

If you find the traditional way of doing long multiplication difficult, use the grid method.

eg: 271 x 52

=	200	70	1
50	10000	3500	50
2	400	140	2
	10400	3640	52

= 14092

Practice Questions

1) 846 ÷ 47 = [ ]

2) 903 ÷ 42 = [ ]

3) 744 ÷ [ ] = 24

4) 279 x 46 = [ ]

5) 387 x 79 = [ ]

6) 457 x [ ] = 5484

Simple formulae

Formulae can be written in words or in letters. To achieve Level 5 you may be required to make up your own formulae in the tests. This is easier than it sounds! Let's start by working through this example.

Question: Write a formula for finding the cost (C) of being on the internet if there is a 20p connection charge and a charge of 3p per minute (M).

1 Read the question and then read it again.

2 Notice what the formula is to find.

You are finding the cost so write C =

3 Decide how many other terms make the formula and work out what the terms are.

There is a 20p connection charge so there is a term of 20
There is a charge of 3p per minute so there is a term of
3 × M = 3M

4 Decide whether the terms should be added, subtracted, multiplied or divided.

The terms need to be added to find the total cost.
20 + 3M

5 Put this together to make your formula.

C = 20 + 3M

TOP TIP 1

★ Talk through your formula in your head.
★ Think clearly.
★ Take it step-by-step.

TOP TIP 2

It helps to only use letters that relate to the information in the question, e.g. C = Cost.

A simple formula is often used to find out the total cost of items bought. In words this formula can be written:

"The total cost is the price of one item multiplied by the number of those items bought."

In letter formulae this could be written as: $T = N \times P$

T = total cost   P = price of each item   N = number of items bought

Practice Question 1

Use the $T = P \times N$ formula to work out these questions.

1) What is the value of **T** if **N** = 15 and **P** = £20?

2) What is the value of **N** if **T** = £12.50 and **P** = £2.50?

3) What is the value of **P** if **T** = £35 and **N** = 5?

Example questions

Paul is using a formula that multiplies a number by 3 and then adds 5. Write this formula.
Use N for the number Paul starts with and A for the answer.

A = $(N \times 3) + 5 = 3N + 5$

Practice Question 2

Ryan uses a formula that multiplies a number by eight and then subtracts 10.
Write this formula.

Use N for the number Ryan starts with and A for the answer.

A =

TOP TIP

If a number and a letter are next to each other, e.g. 4N, it means they are multiplied. Why is the × (multiply) symbol left out? It could get confused with the letter x!!

Units of measure

You will have to answer questions that ask you to compare metric units of measurement (kilograms, grams, litres and centimetres) with imperial units of measurement (miles, pounds, pints).

Question: The school bus travels 20 miles every school day. How far does it travel in a week? ☐

1 Read the question then read it again.

20 miles x 5 days = 100 miles

2 Study the units.

1 mile is about 1.6km

3 Calculate the answer.

100 x 1.6 = 160

4 Remember the units you need for the answer.

160km

5 If your answer looks sensible, write it in the box.

If not, go back to step 2 again.

Practice Questions

1) Approximately how many litres is 14 pints?

☐ pints

2) I need 3 ounces of fruit to make a smoothie. How many grams of fruit should I buy to make 4 smoothies?

☐ grams

3) Liam cycles 5 miles to work and 5 miles back each day. How far does he cycle in a day?

☐ kilometres

4) A new baby weighs 9lbs. How much is this in kg?

☐ kg

TOP TIP

Revision rhymes!   A metre is just 3 feet 3. It's longer than a yard you see!
2 and a bit pounds of jam is round about 1 kilo of ham!

Graphs

You will need to look at graphs like the one below and answer questions about them.

Question: These road signs are in miles. Use the conversion graph to rewrite the road signs in kilometres.

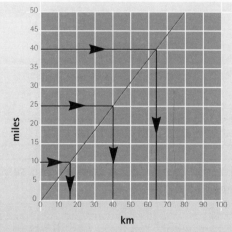

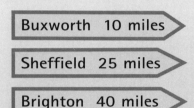

Buxworth 10 miles

Sheffield 25 miles

Brighton 40 miles

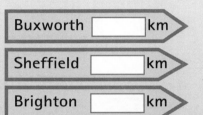

Buxworth [   ] km

Sheffield [   ] km

Brighton [   ] km

1 (Read the question then read it again.)

2 (Be methodical.)

3 (Does the answer look sensible? If so, fill in the answer box.)

Conversion graph tells us that we need to convert values.

Buxworth
- We need to change 10 miles into kilometres.
- Go up the y axis (miles) and find 10.
- Mark this point on the y axis with your pencil.
- Go across to then conversion line and make another mark. Now go down to find the value in kilometres.
  Our answer is 16.
- Now repeat for Sheffield and Brighton.

Check your answers carefully on the graph before writing them in the boxes. The test marker is looking for an EXACT answer.

Practice Questions

The exchange rate for pounds to euros is £1 = €1.6. Using the graph above to help you, draw a new graph to convert pounds to euros. Use the graph to find out how much you would receive when you exchange:

1) £15 = [   ]   2) £35 = [   ]

3) €40 = [   ]   4) €64 = [   ]

Decimals

To achieve Level 6 you must be able to order decimals.

Question: Some decimals are written on cards. Place the decimals in order of size, smallest first.

3.6	3.58	3.21	3.612	3.205

1 (Read the question and then read it again.)

3.600, 3.580, 3.210, 3.612, 3.205

2 (Add zeros to give each number the same number of digits.)

3.210, 3.205, 3.580, 3.600, 3.612

3 (Compare whole numbers and digits in the tenths place)

3.205, 3.210, 3.580, 3.600, 3.612

4 (Now compare digits to the hundredths place and the thousandths place.)

3.205, 3.210, 3.580, 3.600, 3.612

5 (Check that all numbers are included.)

3.205, 3.21, 3.58, 3.6, 3.612

6 (If the answer looks right, write it in the box.)

Rewrite back as normal.

Practice Questions

For each of the questions below, put the decimals in order of size, smallest first.

1) 2.3, 2.52, 2.06, 2.11

2) 3.72, 3.07, 3.7, 3.57

3) 2.71, 2.09, 3.62, 3.602, 3.621

4) 5.6, 5.06, 5.12, 5.125, 5.27

TOP TIP

Always check that you have included all the numbers.

One quantity as a percentage of another

Lots of questions will ask you to express one number as a fraction or percentage of another number.

Question: In a class of 32 students, 15 are girls. What percentage of the class are girls? ☐

---

1 (Read the question then read it again.)

What percentage are girls?

2 (Write the information as a fraction.)

15 out of 32 can be written as $\frac{15}{32}$

3 (To change a fraction to a percentage, multiply by 100%.)

$\frac{15}{32} \times 100\% = 46.875$

4 (Round off the answer to a sensible number.)

$= 46.9\%$

5 (Check you have answered the question properly.)

Our answer is about 47%, which is just under a half.

6 (If the answer looks sensible, write it in the box.)

Our answer is 46.9% (to 1 dp).

Practice Questions

Answer these questions, rounding your answer to the nearest whole number.

1) Write 26 out of 42 as a percentage. ☐

2) Write 17 out of 63 as a percentage. ☐

3) There are 14 boys in a class of 35. What percentage are boys? ☐

4) A jumper is priced at £45. £20 is taken off in a sale.
   What percentage of the original price is the reduction? ☐

KEY FACT

To change an amount to a percentage, multiply by 100%.

TOP TIP

Always check that your answer looks sensible.

Adding and subtracting fractions

You need to be able to add and subtract fractions by writing them with a common denominator.

Remember how to change fractions into equivalents

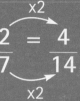

$$\frac{2}{7} = \frac{4}{14}$$

x2

x2

Question: Work out the answer to $\dfrac{7}{9} + \dfrac{3}{4} = \boxed{}$

1 Read the question then read it again.

Add the fractions.

2 Think about the question.

The denominators are not the same.

3 Study the numbers and decide on a common denominator.

36 is the lowest common denominator.

4 Change the fractions to their equivalents, so the denominator is the same.

$$\frac{7}{9} \; ^{x4}_{x4} = \frac{28}{36} \quad \text{and} \quad \frac{3}{4} \; ^{x9}_{x9} = \frac{27}{36}$$

the fractions now have the same denominator.

5 Add the numerators.

$$\frac{28}{36} + \frac{27}{36} = \frac{55}{36}$$

6 Simplify your answer if possible.

7 If your answer looks sensible, write it in the box

$\frac{55}{36}$ is the same as $1\frac{19}{36}$

Practice Questions

1) $\dfrac{2}{3} + \dfrac{3}{5} = \boxed{}$

2) $\dfrac{3}{4} - \dfrac{1}{3} = \boxed{}$

3) $\dfrac{4}{9} + \dfrac{1}{5} = \boxed{}$

4) $2\dfrac{1}{2} - 1\dfrac{1}{3} = \boxed{}$

5 $\dfrac{7}{12} - \dfrac{1}{3} = \boxed{}$

Equivalent fractions, decimals and percentages

You should understand and use the equivalences between fractions, decimals and percentages.

Question: Convert the fraction $\frac{12}{17}$ into a decimal and then a percentage. Round your answer to two decimal places.

$$\frac{12}{17} = \boxed{}$$

1 Read the question and read it again.

Change $\frac{12}{17}$ into a decimal and percentage.

2 Look at the number. Is it over a half?

$\frac{12}{17}$ is over one half so the answer should be over 50%

3 Divide the numerator by the denominator.

$\frac{12}{17}$ = 0.70588... Do not round the answer until the end.

4 To change to a percentage, multiply by 100%.

Multiply 0.70588... by 100% = 70.588

5 Check the answer to see if its sensible.

The answer is over 50% and looks about right.

6 Write your answers in the box. Remember to round to two decimal places.

$\frac{12}{17}$ as a decimal is 0.71 (2dp)

$\frac{12}{17}$ as a percentage is 70.59% (2dp)

KEY FRACTIONS AND THEIR EQUIVALENTS

Fraction	Decimal	Percentage
$\frac{1}{2}$	0.5	50%
$\frac{1}{4}$	0.25	25%
$\frac{3}{4}$	0.75	75%
$\frac{1}{3}$	$0.\dot{3}$	33.3%
$\frac{2}{3}$	$0.\dot{6}$	66.6%
$\frac{1}{8}$	0.125	12.5%

Ratio

To achieve Level 6 you should be able to calculate using ratios in appropriate situations.

Question: £55 is to be shared between three people in the ratio 2:3:6. How much do they each get?

1 Read the question then read it again.

£55... three people... ratio 2 : 3 : 6

2 Add up the total parts.

2 + 3 + 6 = 11 parts

3 Divide to work out one part.

£55 ÷ 11 = £5. One part is worth £5.

4 Work out what the other parts are worth.

2 parts = 2 x 5 = £10
3 parts = 3 x 5 = £15
6 parts = 6 x 5 = £30

5 Check by adding up the amounts.

£10 + £15 + £30 = £55✓
which totals the money to be shared out.

6 Write your answer in the box.

Write £10, £15 and £30

Practice Questions

1) Share £28 in the ratio 4:3

2) Share £100 in the ratio 12:13

3) To bake a flan for four people I need 1200g of flour.
   How much flour would I need if I was baking a flan for six people?

4) Five oranges cost 85p. Work out the cost of eleven similar oranges.

5) Seven pencils cost £1.12. Work out the cost of fifteen similar pencils.

6) An orchard has apple and pear trees in the ratio 4:7.
   If there are 660 trees, how many are pear trees?

TOP TIP

To help solve ratio problems, work out what one part is worth.

Finding the nth term of a linear sequence

Here we look at a rule which lets you find any term of a number pattern without writing down each term. This is called finding a general rule of the nth term of a sequence.

Question: Write down the nth term of this sequence:
5, 8, 11, 14, 17...

1 (Read the question then read it again.)

Find the nth term.

2 (Study the number.)

What is the difference between the numbers?
5, 8, 11, 14, 17
    3 3 3 3

3 (Multiply the difference by one.)

Test with the first term: n =1, 3 x 1 = 3.
Now check what the first term is.

4 (Adjust the rule.)

Adjust the rule by adding 2 to give 5, $3n+2$;
3 x 1 + 2 = 5 ✔
so $3n + 2 = 5$ when n is the first term.

5 (Test the rule by using $n = 2$)

$n = 2$,   (3 x 2) + 2 = 8 ✔ correct

6 (If the rule works, write it in the box.)

$3n + 2$ is the nth term of the sequence
5, 8, 11, 14...

TOP TIP 1 When the difference is the same, this gives the number (a) which we multiply by n, ie: an.

TOP TIP 2 The nth term of a linear sequence is $an+b$, where a is the difference and b is the value that needs to be added to give the correct value in the sequence.

Practice Questions Find the nth term of these sequences.

1) 2, 4, 6, 8, 10

3) 3, 7, 11, 15, 19

2) 5, 7, 9, 11, 13

4) 1, 3, 5, 7, 9

Linear equations

At Level 6 you should be able to set up and solve linear equations.

Question: Solve the equation $5n + 2 = 12$ $n =$ [   ]

1 Read the question and read it again.

$5n + 2 = 12$

2 Use the balance method.

subtract 2 from both sides:
$5n + 2 - 2 = 12 - 2$

3 Make the equation '$n =$ '

$5n = 10$ divide both sides by 5
$n = 2$

4 Does the answer look sensible? Check by substituting back into the equation.

substitute $n = 2$ into $5n + 2$
$5 \times 2 + 2 = 12$ ✓
The answer is correct.

5 If the answer works, write it in the box.

$n = 2$

Practice Questions

Solve:

1) $3n = 12$ $n =$ [   ]

2) $4n = 12$ $n =$ [   ]

3) $4n = 28$ $n =$ [   ]

4) $2n + 1 = 7$ $n =$ [   ]

5) $3n - 2 = 13$ $n =$ [   ]

6) $7n + 1 = 22$ $n =$ [   ]

7) $3 - 4n = 11$ $n =$ [   ]

8) $4 - 2n = 12$ $n =$ [   ]

TOP TIP 1
The aim is to get the letter to be found on its own.

TOP TIP 2
Remember to do the same thing to both sides of the equation, otherwise it is not balanced.

Question: Solve the equation $6x - 3 = 3x + 15$ $x =$

1 (Read the question and read it again.)

$6x - 3 = 3x + 15 \ +3$

2 (Use the balance method to get the numbers together on the right hand side of the equation.)

(Add 3) $6x = 3x + 15 + 3$
            $6x = 3x + 18$

3 (Use the balance method to get the letters together on the left hand side of the equation.)

(Subtract $3x$) $3x = 18$

4 (Make the equation '$x =$ ')

(divide by 3) $x = \frac{18}{3}$ $\therefore x = 6$

5 (Does the answer look sensible? Check by substituting back into the equation.)

Substitute $x = 6$
$(6 \times 6) - 3 = (3 \times 6) + 15$ ✓

6 (If the answer works, write it in the box.)

$x = 6$

Practice Questions

Solve:

1) $3n = 12$ $n =$

2) $5n - 4 = 16$ $n =$

3) $2n - 1 = 9$ $n =$

4) $5n + 2 = 3n + 6$ $n =$

5) $3n - 5 = 2n + 4$ $n =$

6) $4n - 1 = 3 - 2n$ $n =$

7) $\frac{2n}{5} + 2 = 5$ $n =$

8) $3(2n + 1) = 9$ $n =$

TOP TIP 3

If the equation has brackets, multiply out the brackets first and solve as normal.

For example $3(2n + 1) = 12$ becomes $6n + 3 = 12$

Drawing linear graphs

You should be able to draw a linear graph and interpret the general details.

Question: Draw the graph $y = 2x - 1$ if x is between 3 and −3

1 Read the question then read it again.

2 Choose the x coordinates.

Use $x = 3, 0$ and −3 as the starting values. You need at least three.

3 Substitute the x coordinates into the equation.

when $x = 3$ $y = 2 \times 3 - 1 = 5$
when $x = 0$ $y = 2 \times 0 - 1 = -1$
when $x = -3$ $y = 2 \times -3 - 1 = -7$

4 Put the results in a table.

x	−3	0	3
y	−7	−1	5

5 Plot the coordinates.

Plot the points
(-3, -7) (0, -1) (3, 5)

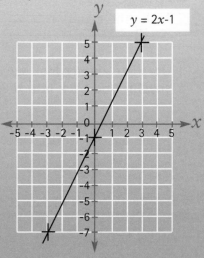

$y = 2x\text{-}1$

6 Join the coordinates with a straight line and label.

7 Check that all the points lie on a straight line.

Practice Questions
On the grid opposite, draw these graphs:

1) $y = x + 2$

2) $y = 2x + 1$

3) $y = x - 4$

4) $y = 4 - 2x$

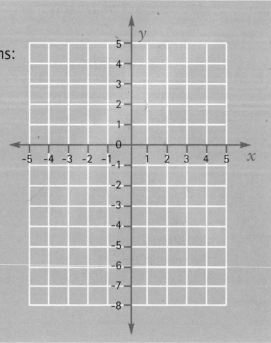

You also need to be able to interpret linear graphs.
Remember: the equation of a straight-line graph is:

$y = mx + c$ m is the gradient or steepness
                    c is the intercept on the y axis

Question: Find the equation of this straight line.

1 (Read the question then read it again.)

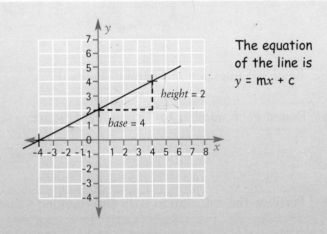

The equation of the line is $y = mx + c$

2 (Find the gradient of the line.)

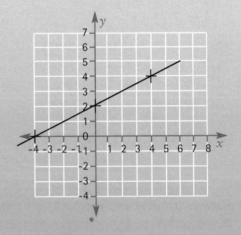

To find the gradient m, draw in a triangle and work out the height and base.

Gradient = $\dfrac{\text{height}}{\text{base}}$ = $\dfrac{2}{4}$

Gradient = $\dfrac{1}{2}$

3 (Find the intercept on the y axis.)

The graph crosses the y axis at (0,2)

4 (Write down the equation.)

$y = \dfrac{1}{2}x + 2$

5 (Double check that it sounds about right.)

Practice Questions
Find the equations of these lines:

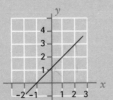   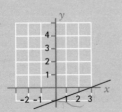   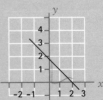

Equation =

1) [   ]   2) [   ]   3) [   ]

KEY FACT

When the gradient is positive, the graph slopes in this direction.

When the gradient is negative, the graph slopes in this direction.

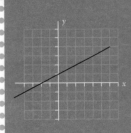   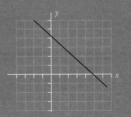

Significant figures and estimating

For Level 7 you need to be able to round to one significant figure and multiply and divide mentally.

Question: By rounding each number to 1 significant figure, estimate the answer to $\dfrac{292 \times 51.8}{9.61 \times 2.14}$ = [ ]

1 Read the question and read it again.

Rounding... significant figure... estimate

2 Round each number to 1 significant figure.

292 = 300 (1 sf)
51.8 = 50 (1 sf)
9.61 = 10 (1 sf)
2.14 = 2 (1 sf)

3 Perform the calculation with the rounded values.

$\dfrac{300 \times 50}{10 \times 2} = \dfrac{15000}{20} = 750$

4 Does the answer look sensible? If not, try again.

750 sounds about right.

5 Write the answer in the box.

Write 750 in the box.

KEY FACT 1

The 1st significant figure is the first digit which is not a zero. The 2nd, 3rd, 4th... significant figures follow on after the 1st digit. They may or may not be zeros.

KEY FACT 2

When rounding, apply the same rule as with decimal places. If the next digit is 5 or more, round up.

TOP TIP

When rounding to significant figures you must retain the size of the number,

ie: 276 = 300 (1 sf) not 3!

Practice Questions

Round each number to 1 sf and estimate the answer to these calculations:

1) 2.7 x 4.9 [ ]

2) $(62.1)^2$ [ ]

3) $\dfrac{294.2 \times 37.1}{4.02}$ [ ]

4) $(71.1 \times 9.6)^2$ [ ]

Multiplying and dividing by numbers between 0 and 1

For Level 7 you need to understand the effects of multiplying and dividing by numbers between 0 and 1.

Question: Work out the answer to this calculation:

$$27 \times 0.02 = \boxed{}$$

1 Read the question and read it again. — Multiply by a number less than 1.

2 Picture the number and what will happen. — Multiplying by a number less than 1 makes the answer smaller. Think about the decimal place.

3 Calculate. — Multiply $27 \times 2 = 54.0$

4 Adjust the position of the digits. — Move the digits two places to the right.

5 Check your answer. —
$27 \times 2 = 54.0$
$27 \times 0.02 = 0.54$

6 If the answer looks sensible, write it in the box.

KEY FACT 1

When you multiply by numbers between 0 and 1 things get smaller.

KEY FACT 2

When you divide by numbers between 0 and 1 things get bigger.

TOP TIP

When dividing by numbers less than 1, the digits move to the left,

eg: $24 \div 0.02 = 1200$

$24 \div 2 = 12$

Now move digits two places to the left = 1200

Practice Questions

1) $29 \times 0.3 = \boxed{}$

2) $44 \div 0.2 = \boxed{}$

3) $42 \times 0.002 = \boxed{}$

4) $33 \div 0.003 = \boxed{}$

5) $62 \times 0.02 = \boxed{}$

6) $2100 \div 0.3 = \boxed{}$

7) $47 \times 0.03 = \boxed{}$

8) $48 \div 0.004 = \boxed{}$

Proportional changes

For Level 7 you need to be able to use and understand proportional changes.

Increasing and decreasing by a percentage

Firstly you need to find the multiplier.

- An increase of 15% is like adding 15% to 100%, which is what you started with. You will end up to with 100% + 15% = 115%.

$$115\% = \frac{115}{100} = 1.15, \text{ so you need to multiply by } 1.15$$

- A decrease of 20% is like taking 20% away from the 100% you started with and you will end up with 80%. 80% is 0.8, so you will need to multiply by 0.8.

Question: **The price of a jacket is £62. In the winter sales it is reduced in price by 15%. Work out the reduced price of the jacket.**

1 Read the question carefully.	It is a % change problem.
2 Look at the numbers.	The answer should be less than £62.
3 Work out the multiplier.	It's a price reduction, so multiplier is less than 1 = (100 – 15) = 85% = 0.85
4 Write the problem as a decimal multiplication.	0.85 × 62 = £52.70
5 Does the answer sound sensible? If so, write it down.	Answer sounds ok.

TOP TIP 1
Take care with single figure percentages. An increase of 2% is 1.02 not 1.2.

TOP TIP 2   When finding the reverse percentage, ie the price before the reduction you need to divide by the multiplier. For example, a cooker costs £420 after a 20% reduction. What was the original cost of the cooker?

Original price = 420 ÷ 0.8 = £525

Repeated percentage change

This is when the percentage increase or decrease is repeated over a period of time.

Question: A car is bought for £12500. Each year it depreciates in value by 12%. How much is the car worth after three years?

1	Read the question then read it again.	It is a <u>repeated</u> % change problem.
2	Look at the numbers.	The car's value depreciates (goes down) by 12% over three years.
3	Work out the multiplier.	Price reduction, so multiplier is less than 1 = (100 − 12) = 88% = 0.88
4	Write out the calculation.	12500 × (0.88)³ (original) × (multiplier) (number of years) price
5	Work out the answer.	Use the power key on your calculator 12500 × (0.88)³ = £8518.40
6	Check that the answer sounds sensible and write it down	£8518.40 sounds ok.

Practice Questions

1) Increase £25 by 12%

2) Decrease £47 by 8%

3) A house is bought for £104000. Each year it increases in price by 8%.
   Work out how much the house is worth after two years.

4) A coat costs £55 after a reduction of 10%.
   Work out the original price of the coat.

The efficient use of a calculator

For Level 7 you need to be able to solve numerical problems and use a calculator efficiently.

Question: Using a calculator work out $\dfrac{2.7 + 4.2}{6.9 - 3.4}$ = [ ]

1 Read the question then read it again.

Rewrite the question and insert brackets:
$$\frac{(2.7 + 4.2)}{(6.9 - 3.4)}$$

2 Use the bracket or memory keys on your calculator.

Decide which keys to use: brackets or memory keys.

3 Type in the numbers carefully. Check your answer to see if it's sensible.

With brackets type in:

[	2.7	+	4.2	]	÷	[	6.9	-	3.4	]	=

With the memory keys type in:

6.9	-	3.4	=	MIN	2.7	+	4.2	=	÷	MR	=

4 Complete the calculation and enter your answer.

The answer is 1.97 (2dp)

KEY FACT

B – Brackets
O – Powers
D – Division
M – Multiplication
A – Addition
S – Subtraction

This shows the order in which calculations must be done: brackets should be done first then powers, then division, etc

Shift or 2nd or Inv allow 2nd functions to be carried out.

– or +/- changes positive numbers to negative ones.

Bracket keys

Often puts the x10 part in when working in standard form.

Pressing SHIFT EXP often gives π

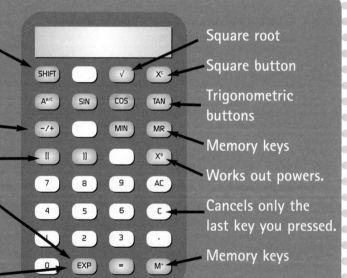

Square root

Square button

Trigonometric buttons

Memory keys

Works out powers.

Cancels only the last key you pressed.

Memory keys

TOP TIP

Make sure you try both methods and that you can use your calculator efficiently.

Practice Questions

Using both the brackets and memory keys work out the correct answers to 2dp:

1) $\dfrac{3.7 + 4.9}{(1.2)^2}$ = [ ]

2) $\dfrac{15.6 - 2.7}{3.2 \times 1.4}$ = [ ]

3) $\dfrac{(12.5)^2 - (1.2)^2}{3.2 + 1.6}$ = [ ]

Finding the nth term of a quadratic sequence

KEY FACT

You need to be able to find the nth term of a number pattern when the rule is quadratic.

The nth term of a quadratic sequence is $an^2 \times bn + c$, where b or c may be equal to zero.

Question: Write down the nth term of this sequence:

3, 9, 19, 33, 51...

1 Read the question then read it again.

Find the nth term.

2 Study the numbers and find the first difference between the terms.

3,ᵥ 9,ᵥ 19,ᵥ 33,ᵥ 51
$\quad$ 6 $\quad$ 10 $\quad$ 14 $\quad$ 18 $\quad$ 1st difference

3 Now find the second difference (ie, the differences of the differences).

$\quad$ v $\quad$ v $\quad$ v
$\quad$ 4 $\quad$ 4 $\quad$ 4 $\quad$ 2nd difference

4 Halve the second difference to find the number in front of n^2

2nd difference = 4
Number in front of n^2 = 4 ÷ 2 = 2

5 Test with the first term.

If $n = 1$ $\quad$ $2n^2 = 2 \times 1^2 = 2$

6 Adjust the rule.

We need 3 so we add 1
$2n^2 + 1$

7 Test the rule by using $n = 2$

$n = 2$ .. $2 \times 2^2 + 1 = 9$

8 If the rule works, write it in the box.

$2n^2 + 1$ is the nth term of the sequence 3, 9, 19, 33...

Practice Questions Find the nth term of these sequences:

1) 1, 4, 9, 16, 25 ...

2) 5, 11, 21, 35, 53 ...

3) −1, 5, 15, 29, 47 ...

4) -3, 0, 5, 12, 21 ...

KEY FACT

The nth term of a quadratic sequence is $an^2 \times bn + c$, where b or c may be equal to zero.

Multiplying out brackets

KEY FACT 1

Single Brackets

When multiplying out single brackets, multiply everything inside the bracket by everything outside the bracket.

$2(x+3) = 2x + 6$

KEY FACT 2

Two Brackets

When you have two brackets, each term in the first bracket is multiplied with each term in the second bracket.

$$(x + 2)(x + 3) = x(x+3) + 2(x + 3)$$
$$= x^2 + 3x + 2x + 6$$
$$= x^2 + 5x + 6$$

Question: Multiply out these brackets $(x - 4)(x + 2) = $ [ ]

1 Read the question then read it again.

2 Rewrite the question.

3 Multiply out each bracket.

4 Simplify the expression.

5 Check the answer, particularly where there are negatives.

6 Write the answer in the box.

Beware of the negative 4!

Write as $x(x + 2) - 4(x + 2)$

$x^2 + 2x - 4x - 8$

$= x^2 - 2x - 8$

Double check $2x - 4x = 2x$

Answer is $x^2 - 2x - 8$

TOP TIP 1 There are other ways of multiplying brackets, ie: the grid method

×	x	+3
x	x^2	+3x
+2	+2x	+6

$= x^2 + 5x + 6$

Use the one you are happy with!

TOP TIP 2

Remember the rules of positive and negative numbers:

$+ × + = +$
$- × - = +$
$+ × - = -$
$- × + = -$

Practice Questions

Multiply out the following:

1) $2(x + 1)$ [ ]

2) $3(x - 2)$ [ ]

3) $-4(x - 4)$ [ ]

4) $(2 + x)(3 - x)$ [ ]

5) $(x - 4)(x - 5)$ [ ]

6) $(x - 6)(x - 2)$ [ ]

7) $(x + y)(x - y)$ [ ]

Solving inequalities

KEY FACT

> means greater than

< means less than

≥ means greater than or equal to

≤ means less than or equal to

so $x > 2$ and $2 < x$ both say x is greater than 2.

Question: Solve the inequality $4 - 2x \leq 8$ [   ]

---

1 (Read the question then read it again.)

2 (To solve like an equation, you need to do the same calculation on both sides.)

3 (Check carefully if dividing or multiplying by a negative number.)

4 (Does the answer seem sensible? If so, write it in the box.)

Need to have an inequality with 'x'

$4 - 2x \leq 8$

$-2x \leq 8 - 4$ (subtract 4)

$-2x \leq 4$

$x \geq -2$ (divide by -2)

Since we divided by -2 we change all signs, including the inequality sign.

$x \geq -2$

Practice Questions

Solve these inequalities:

1) $2x < 10$ [   ]

2) $3x \leq 9$ [   ]

3) $4x - 1 \leq 19$ [   ]

4) $5x - 2 \geq 13$ [   ]

5) $5 - 2x < 10$ [   ]

6) $3x < 9$ [   ]

7) $-2x \leq 6$ [   ]

8) $4 + 2x \geq 6$ [   ]

9) $3 - x \leq 5$ [   ]

10) $4x + 1 \geq 5$ [   ]

TOP TIP 1

Solve inequalities like an equation.

TOP TIP 2

If multiplying or dividing by a negative, the inequality sign changes direction.

Simultaneous equations

Equations with two unknowns are called simultaneous equations. They can be solved algebraically or graphically.

Question: Solve simultaneously $2x + y = 8$

$x - 2y = -6$

Algebraic method

1 (Read the question then read it again.)

2 (Label the questions (1) and (2))

3 (Since no coefficient match, swap over x values and multiply. Rename questions (3) and (4).)

4 (The coefficient of x in equations (3) and (4) are the same. Subtract equation (4) from equation (3) and then solve the remaining equation.)

5 (Substitute the value of $y = 4$ into equation (1) or equation (2). Solve this equation to find x.)

6 (Check in equation (1).)

7 (Write down the solution.)

We need to find the values of x and y

$$
\begin{aligned}
2x + y &= 8 & &(1) \\
x - 2y &= -6 & &(2)
\end{aligned}
$$

$$
\begin{aligned}
2x + y &= 8 & &(1) \times 1 \\
x - 2y &= -6 & &(2) \times 2
\end{aligned}
$$

$$
\begin{aligned}
2x + y &= 8 & &(3) \\
2x - 4y &= -12 & &(4) \\
5y &= 20 \\
y &= 4
\end{aligned}
$$

$$
\begin{aligned}
2x + 4 &= 8 \\
2x &= 4 \\
x &= 2
\end{aligned}
$$

$2 \times 2 + 4 = 8 \checkmark$

$x = 2, y = 4$

TOP TIP 1
To eliminate terms with the opposite signs, add the equations.

TOP TIP 2
To eliminate terms with the same signs, subtract the equations.

The points at which any two graphs intersect represent the simultaneous solutions of these equations.

Question: Solve the simultaneous equations by a graphical method $x + y = 6$
$2x + y = 8$

Graphical method

1 (Read the question then read it again.)

Solve the simultaneous equation by a graphical method.

2 (Draw the graphs.)

First find the coordinates of the graphs
$x + y = 6$ $(0, 6)$ $(6, 0)$ $(2, 4)$
$2x + y = 8$ $(0, 8)$ $(4, 0)$

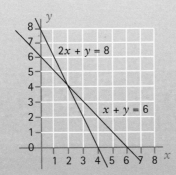

Now plot these points and connect them with a line.
$x = 0$ $y = 8$
$y = 0$ $x = 4$

3 (Write down the coordinates of the points of intersection.)

The coordinates of the point of the intersection is $(2, 4)$ This is the simultaneous solution of the equations $x = 2, y = 4$

4 (Check by substituting into the equations.)

$2 + 4 = 6$ ✓
$4 + 4 = 8$ ✓

Practice Questions

Solve these simultaneous equations   a) graphically   b) algebraically

1) $2x + y = 6$
    $x + y = 4$

2) $2x + y = 4$
    $3x - y = 1$

3) $2x - 3y = 7$
    $x - y = 4$

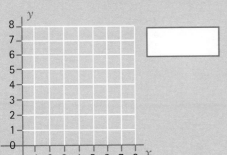

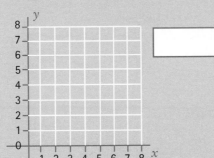

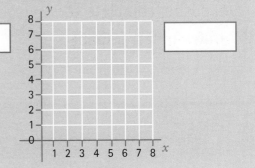

2-D Representations of 3-D objects

You should be able to make 3-D objects by drawing a net. You also need to understand front, side and top elevations for a 3-D shape. This page highlights the important points you need to know.

Nets of solids

The **net** of a 3-D shape is the 2-D (flat) shape, which is folded to make the 3-D shape.

Plans and elevations

A **plan** is what is seen if a 3-D shape is looked down on from above.

An **elevation** is seen if the 3-D shape is looked at from the side or front.

Isometric drawings

An easy way to draw 3-D shapes is by using isometric paper. The shape that is drawn is known as an **isometric projection**.

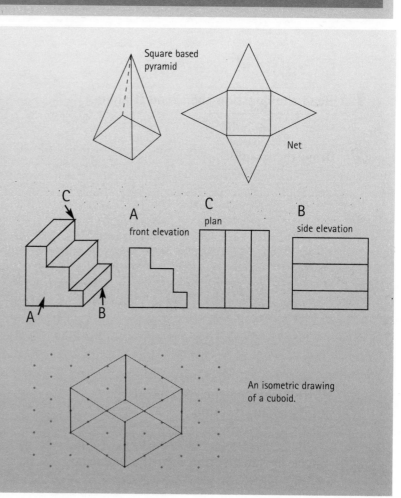

Practice Questions

1 Draw a net of a cuboid.

2 On the isometric paper opposite, complete the drawing of a T shape.

Triangles and quadrilaterals

For Level 6 you need to know the properties of triangles and quadrilaterals and be able to recognise quadrilaterals from their properties.

Triangle

There are several types of triangles.

   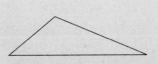

Equilateral	Isosceles	Right-angles	Scalene
3 sides equal 3 angles equal	2 sides equal base angles equal	Has a 90⁰ angle	No sides or angles the same

Quadrilaterals

 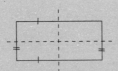 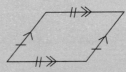 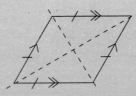

Square	Rectangle	Parallelogram	Rhombus
4 lines of symmetry Rotational symmetry of order 4	2 lines of symmetry Rotational symmetry of order 2	No lines of symmetry Rotational symmetry of order 2	2 lines of symmetry Rotational symmetry of order 2

 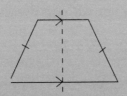

Kite

1 line of symmetry
No rotational symmetry

Trapezium

Has 1 line of symmetry
No rotational symmetry

TOP TIP 1

Try and learn these properties of different quadrilaterals by testing yourself with a friend.

TOP TIP 2

Remember to show which sides are parallel and equal in length

Polygons

These are 2-D shapes with straight sides. Regular polygons are shapes with all sides and angles equal.

To achieve Level 6 you need to know the names of different polygons and how to calculate their interior and exterior angles.

Number of sides	Name of polygon
3	Triangle
4	Quadrilateral
5	Pentagon
6	Hexagon
7	Heptagon
8	Octagon
9	Nonagon
10	Decagon

When the polygon is not regular the angles are different sizes.

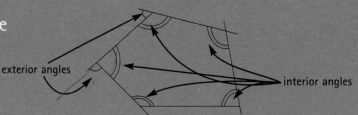

exterior angles   interior angles

Question: Work out the size of the interior and exterior angles of a regular pentagon.

1 Read the question then read it again.

2 Picture the shape and remember the formula to find exterior angles.

Exterior angle size $= \dfrac{360°}{n}$

Where n is equal to the number of sides.

3 How many sides has the shape got and is it regular?

Pentagon has 5 sides and since it is regular we can divide 360° by 5.

4 Calculate your answer.

$360° \div 5 = 72°$

5 Now calculate the interior angle.

Interior + exterior = 180° so
Interior angle = 180° - 72°
             = 108°

6 Check your answer.

$108° + 72° = 180°$ ✓

7 If your answers check out, write them in the box.

If not, return to step 3.

KEY FACT

Sum of interior angles $= (n - 2) \times 180°$

Sum of exterior angles $= \dfrac{360°}{n}$

Exterior angle + interior angle = 180°

Intersecting lines and parallel lines

KEY FACTS

Vertically opposite angles are equal.

$a = b$ $c = d$

For angles in parallel lines: Alternate (z) angles are equal.

Corresponding angles are equal.

Supplementary angles add up to 180°. $e + f = 180°$

Question: Work out the size of angles a and b on this diagram.

1 (Read the question then read it again.)

2 (Are the lines parallel?)   Yes, the lines are parallel.

3 (What type of angle is angle a?)   Angle a and 75° lie between two parallel lines so they are supplementary and must add up to 180°

4 (Calculate the answer for angle a.) $a + 75° = 180°$
                                                  $a = 180° - 75° = 105°$

5 (Look at angle b. What type of angle is b?) Angle b is vertically opposite to 75°

6 (Work out angle b.)   Vertically opposite angles are equal, so b = 75°

7 (Check your answers and write them in the box.)   a = 105°, b = 75°

Practice Questions

Calculate the missing angles in these diagrams, giving reasons.

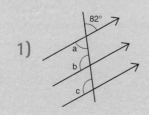

1)

a) [ ]
b) [ ]
c) [ ]

2)

e) [ ]
f) [ ]
f) [ ]

Logo and transformations

At Level 6 you should be able to devise instructions for a computer to draw a shape. You also need to know how to transform shapes using rotations.

Question: Write a LOGO program to draw a square of side 5 units.

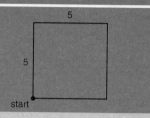

1 Read the question then read it again.

The question uses the computer program LOGO.

2 Think about the instructions to use.

The instructions are:
FORWARD a number of units
LEFT TURN a given number of degrees
RIGHT TURN a given number of degrees

3 Write down the instructions.

FORWARD 5 / RIGHT TURN 90
FORWARD 5 / RIGHT TURN 90
FORWARD 5 / RIGHT TURN 90
FORWARD 5

4 If there are repeats, shorten the instructions.

Rewrite REPEAT [FORWARD 5, RIGHT TURN 90]

5 Check you answer. Have you included all the instructions?

Step by step thinking really helps here!

6 If the answer looks right, write it in the box.

KEY FACTS

A shape can be rotated through an angle about a centre of rotation.

The flag has been rotated 90° clockwise about point P

The flag has been rotated 180° about point P

Practice Question

Rotate shape T through 90° anti-clockwise about the point Q.

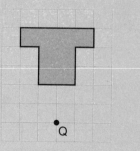

Area of plane shapes

KEY FACTS

You need to know how to find the area of the following shapes using these formulae.

Rectangle	
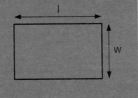	

Area = length x width
A = l x w

Triangle	
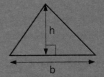	

Area = $\frac{1}{2}$ base x perpendicular height
= $\frac{1}{2}$ x b x h

Parallelogram	
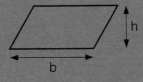	

Area = base x perpendicular height
A = b x h

Trapezium	
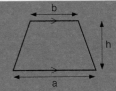	

Area = $\frac{1}{2}$ x ($^{sum\ of\ parallel}_{sides}$) x ($^{distance}_{between\ them}$)

A = $\frac{1}{2}$ x (a + b) x h

Question: Find the area of this trapezium.

10 cm
8 cm

6 cm

---

1 (Read the question then read it again.)

2 (Use the formula.)

3 (Replace the letters in the formula with the lengths.)

4 (Calculate the area.)

5 (Add in the unit of measurement.)

6 (If your answer looks sensible, write it in the box. If not, go back and check that you have used the correct values of a, b and h.)

Find the area of a trapezium.

Use the formula $A = \frac{1}{2} \times (a + b) \times h$

$A = \frac{1}{2} \times (8 + 10) \times 6$

$A = \frac{1}{2} \times (18) \times 6$ $A = \frac{108}{2}$

$A = 54$

Area = 54cm²

a = 8, b = 10, h = 6

The circle

You need to be able to find the circumference and area of a circle by using these formulas.

$\pi = 3.14$
to 2 sf.

Circumference = π x diameter   or π x 2 x radius

Area = π x radius x radius   or π x radius²

Question: Find the area of this circle

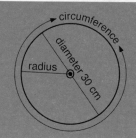

1 Read the question then read it again.

You are finding the area so you need the formula.

2 Remember your formula.

Area of a circle = π x r²

3 Do you need to find the radius?

The radius is half the diameter
Radius = 15cm (30 ÷ 2)

4 Use π = 3.14 and replace the value of r with 15

A = 3.14 x 15²

5 Calculate the answer

A = 3.14 x 225
A = 706.5

6 Add in the unit of measurement.

Area = 706.5cm²

7 Estimate the answer and check your estimate against the answer.

Estimate = 3 x 15²
        = 3 x 225 = 675

8 If your answer looks sensible, write it in the box.

If not, go back to step 4 and try again.

Practice Questions

Find the 1) Circumference   2) Area of these circles. Use π = 3.14

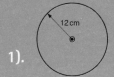

1).

2).

3).

TOP TIPS

When dealing with area, make sure the units are always squared.

Remember that r² = means r x r NOT 2 x r!

Volumes of cubes and cuboids

The volume of a solid is the amount of space the solid can hold.
You need to know these formulas for Level 6.

Volume of a cuboid

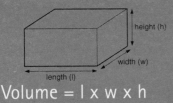

Volume = l x w x h

$V = lwh$

Volume of a cube

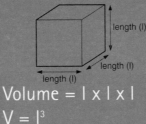

Volume = l x l x l

$V = l^3$

Question: Find the volume of this cuboid.

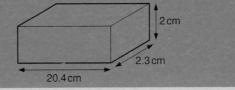

2 cm
2.3 cm
20.4 cm

---

1 (Read the question then read it again.)

You are working with volume,
so you need a formula.

2 (Remember your formula.)

$V = lwh$

3 (Picture the numbers, what do they look like?)

L = 20.4cm is approximately 20cm
W = 2.3cm is approximately 2cm

4 (Study the numbers again and estimate the volume.)

V = 20 x 2 x 2 = 80. The volume is
approximately 80cm³.

5 (Calculate your answer.)

V = l x w x h
= 20.4 x 2.3 x 2
= 93.84

6 (Add in your unit of measurement.)

cm cubed = cm³   93.84cm³

7 (Check your answer against your estimate in step 4)

80 is quite close to 93.84

8 (If your answer looks sensible, write it in the box.)

If not go back to step 4 and try again.

Practice Questions

Try some more questions. Work out the volume of the following:

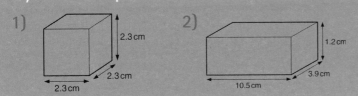

1)   2.3 cm   2.3 cm   2.3 cm

2)   1.2 cm   3.9 cm   10.5 cm

TOP TIPS

When dealing with volume
make sure that that units
are always cubed.
For example: m³, cm³, mm³

Enlargement

Enlargements change the size but not the shape of an object.

The centre of an enlargement is the point from which the enlargement takes place.

The scale factor indicates how many times the lengths of the original figure have changed size.

If the scale factor is greater than 1, the shape becomes bigger.
If the scale factor is less than 1, the shape becomes smaller.

Question: Enlarge triangle ABC by a scale factor of

a) 2

b) $\frac{1}{2}$

about the centre of enlargement (0, 0)

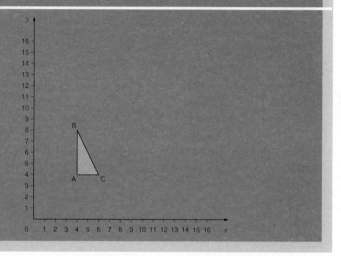

1 (Read the question then read it again.)

Scale factor of 2 makes triangle bigger. Scale factor of $\frac{1}{2}$ makes triangle smaller.

2 (Enlarge the triangle ABC by the scale factor 2. Call it P.)

3 (Enlarge the triangle ABC by a scale factor of 1/2. Call it Q.)

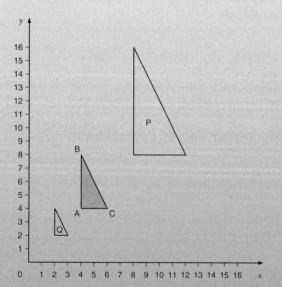

4 (Check that the lengths of triangles P and Q are the correct lengths and the triangles are the correct distances from 0.)

Check that the lengths of triangle P are twice the size of triangle ABC and that the distance from O to P is twice the distance from O to triangle ABC.

Loci

KEY FACTS

1) The locus of a point is the set of all the possible positions which that point can occupy, subject to some given condition or rule. The plural of locus is loci.

2) The locus of the points which are a constant distance from a fixed point is a circle.

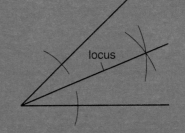

3) The locus of the points which are equidistant from two points A and B is the perpendicular bisector of AB.

perpendicular bisector

A   B

4) The locus of the points which are equidistant from two lines is the line which bisects the angle.

locus

5) The locus of the points which are a constant distance from a continuous line is a pair of parallel lines, above and below the line.

Sample question:

Two radio stations A and B are 60km apart. The range of the transmitter at A is 40km and at B it is 30km. Using a scale of 1cm to 10km, construct a scale diagram to show where signals from both transmitters can be received.

- Draw a circle of radius 4cm at A
- Draw a circle of radius 3km at B
- Shade in the region where they overlap.

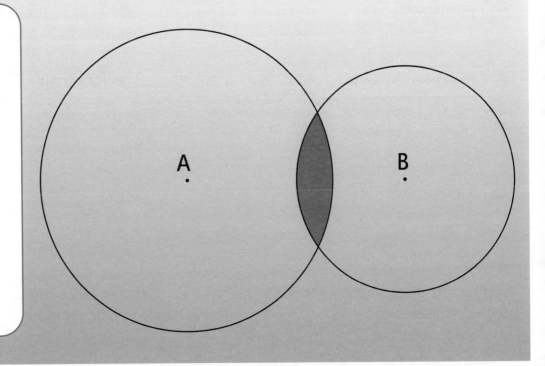

Pythagoras' theorem

For Level 7 you need to be able to apply Pythagoras' theorem when solving problems in two dimensions.

Question: Find the length of the side marked x on the diagram.

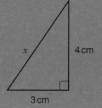

1 (Read the question then read it again.)

Calculate a missing length of a right angled triangle given two other sides.

2 (Is the triangle right angled?)

Pythagoras' theorem only applies to right angled triangles.

3 (Remember the theorem.)

$a^2 + b^2 = c^2$ where c is the hypotenuse.

4 (Square both numbers and add them.)

$= 3^2 + 4^2$
$= 9 + 16$
$= 25$

5 (Square root to find the length of the hypotenuse.)

$\sqrt{25}$
$= 5$. This is the length of the hypotenuse.

6 (Remember the units.)

The lengths of the triangle are in cm.

7 (Check your answer.)

5cm sounds about right: it must be bigger than both shorter sides.

8 (If your answer checks out, write it in the box.)

5cm

TOP TIP 1

Pythagoras' theorem only applies to right angled triangles.
$a^2 + b^2 = c^2$ where c is the hypotenuse.

TOP TIP 2

Remember to square root your answer.

TOP TIP 3

hypotenuse

Question: Find the length of the side marked y on the diagram.

9 cm

y

5 cm

1 Read the question then read it again.

Calculate a missing length of a right angled triangle given two other sides.

2 Is the triangle right angled?

Pythagoras' theorem only applies to right angled triangles.

3 Remember the Theorem.

$a^2 + b^2 = c^2$ where c is the hypotenuse.
So $c^2 - b^2 = a^2$

4 Square both numbers and subtract the smaller one from the larger one.

$9^2 - 5^2$
$= 81 - 25$
$= 56$

5 Square root to find the length of the side.

$\sqrt{56} = 7.48$. This is the length of the missing side.

6 Remember the units.

$y = 7.48$cm

7 Check your answer.

This length needs to be shorter than the hypotenuse of 9cm.

8 If your answer checks out, write it in the box.

Write the answer in the box.

Practice Questions

Find the missing lengths:

1)

8 cm x

5 cm

2)

12 cm   10 cm

x

3)

8.7 cm x

8.2 cm

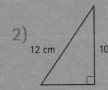

340 km

200 km

start

4) A ship sails 200km due North, then 340km due West.
   Calculate the direct distance of the ship from its starting point.

Accuracy of measurement

In this unit you will learn that measurement is continuous, but remember that measures that are given to the nearest whole number can be in error by up to one half a unit.

Question: Fiona says that her weight is 51kg to the nearest kilogram. Write down the interval in which her true weight (w) must lie and show this on a number line.

1 (Read the question then read it again.)

Fiona's weight is rounded to the nearest kilogram.

2 (Decide on the lower limit.)

Since the weight is 51kg to the nearest kilogram, the smallest number that can be rounded to 51 is 50.5

3 (Decide on the upper limit.)

The largest number that can just be rounded down to 51 is just less than 51.5

4 (Show the interval on a number line.)

The interval in which the true weight (w) lies can be shown on the number line:

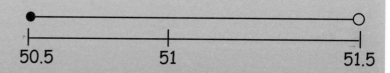

● means 50.5 is included
○ means 51.5 is not included

5 (Write down the interval as an inequality.) 50.5kg ≤ w < 51.5kg

Practice Questions

1) A distance (*d*) is 62km to the nearest km.
   Write down the upper and lower bounds as an inequality.
2) The length of a rectangle is 12.3cm to one decimal place.
   Write down the interval as an inequality in which the true length (*l*) lies.
3) The time of a race is 16.8 seconds, to the nearest tenth of a second. Write down the interval as an inequality in which the true time (*t*) must lie.

KEY FACTS

- The upper bound just means the upper limit.
- The lower bound means the lower limit

Compound measures

At Level 7 you need to be able to use the compound measures of speed and density.

KEY FACT

Speed is a measure of distance and time

speed (s) = $\dfrac{\text{distance (d)}}{\text{time (t)}}$

$S = \dfrac{d}{t}$

KEY FACT

Density is a measure of mass and volume.

Density (D) = $\dfrac{\text{Mass (M)}}{\text{Volume (V)}}$

$D = \dfrac{M}{V}$

Question: A train leaves Watford at 0830 and arrives in Manchester at 1045. Find the average speed of the train if the distance travelled is 180 miles.

1 (Read the question then read it again.)

We need to find the speed.

2 (Check the units.)

Distance is measured in miles, time is measured in hours. Speed will be miles per hour.

3 (Remember your formula.)

$S = \dfrac{d}{t}$

4 (Calculate your answer.)

Speed = $\dfrac{180}{2.25}$ Since 15 minutes is a quarter of an hour we write 0.25 hrs.

5 (Add in your unit of measurement.)

Speed = 80
Speed = 80mph

6 (Check that your answer seems reasonable.)

Speed of train sounds sensible.

Practice Questions

1) Calculate the distance travelled if the speed is 40km/h and the time is 45 minutes.

2) Calculate the density of a wooden block if the Mass is 200g and the volume is 64cm³

3) Calculate the time taken to travel 400km at a speed of 60km/h.

TOP TIPS

- When the speed formula is rearranged we get
  $d = s \times t$ and $t = \dfrac{d}{s}$
- When the density formula is rearranged we get
  $M = D \times V$ $V = \dfrac{M}{D}$

Areas of compound shapes and volumes of prisms

At Level 7 you need to be able to find the area of compound shapes and the volume of prisms.

KEY FACT

A prism is a 3-D shape with a uniform cross-section.

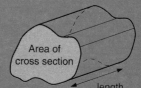

FORMULAS

Prism

Volume = Area of cross-section x length
$V = A \times l$

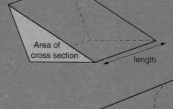

Cylinder

Volume = Area of a circle x length
$V = \pi r^2 \times l$

Question: Find the area of this shape.

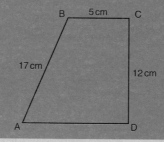

1 (Read the question then read it again.)

Split the diagram up into a triangle and a rectangle.

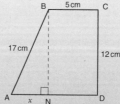

2 (Calculate the length of AN)

Find the length of AN by using Pythagoras' theorem.

$17^2 = 12^2 + x^2$

$17^2 - 12^2 = x^2$

$x = \sqrt{145}$

$x = 12.04 \text{cm}$

3 (Find the area of each part of the shape.)

Triangle $= \frac{1}{2} \times b \times h$

$= \frac{1}{2} \times 12.04 \times 12$

$= 72.24 \text{cm}$

Rectangle $= b \times h$

$= 5 \times 12$

$= 60 \text{cm}^2$

Total Area $= 132.24 \text{ cm}^2$

4 (Check the answer and write down the units.)

Units for Area is squared centimetres.
Area $= 132.24 \text{ cm}^2$

Question: Find the volume of this solid.

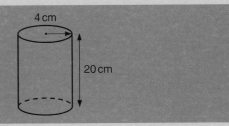

4 cm

20 cm

---

1 (Read the question then read it again.)

Find the volume of a cylinder.

2 (Write down the formula)

$V = \pi r^2 h$

3 (Estimate the volume.)

$V = 3 \times 4^2 \times 20 = 960$
The volume is approximately 960

4 (Calculate the answer.)

$V = 3.14 \times 4^2 \times 20$
$V = 1004.8$

5 (Add in your unit of measurement.)

cm cubed (cm³)
$V = 1004.8 \text{cm}^3$

6 (Check your answer against your estimate.)

Estimate is quite close.

7 (If your answer looks sensible, write it in the box.)

Volume $= 1004.8 \text{cm}^3$

Practice Questions

Find the volume of:

a)

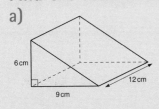

6 cm

12 cm

9 cm

b)

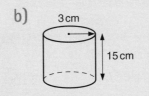

3 cm

15 cm

TOP TIP

Break up complicated shapes into smaller parts when finding the area of a compound shape.

Frequency diagrams for continuous data

You should be able to collect and record continuous data, choosing appropriate class intervals and construct and interpret frequency diagrams.

KEY FACT 1

Continuous data is data that is collected by measuring. Some examples are weight, height, length, etc.

KEY FACT 2

Continuous data is placed in a grouped frequency table with suitable class intervals. Class intervals are usually written as an **inequality** or as an open interval.

Question: The heights (h) in cm of 20 students were:

127 148 142 132 142
142 147 141 138 140
136 148 129 138 139
132 137 125 147 122

Using a class interval of 5cm, make a grouped frequency table to show the data.

1 (Read the question then read it again.)

Need to use class intervals of 5cm.

2 (Look at the range of values.)

Range of height = 148 – 122 = 26cm.

3 (Make up a table.)

Height (cm)	Tally	Frequency
$120 \leq h < 125$	I	1
$125 \leq h < 130$	III	3
$130 \leq h < 135$	II	2
$135 \leq h < 140$	ⅢⅠ	5
$140 \leq h < 145$	ⅢⅠ	5
$145 \leq h < 150$	IIII	4

4 (Carefully fill in the table.)

5 (Check that the total is the same as the number of items.)

Total of frequency column = 20
Which is the total number of students.

TOP TIP 1 Remember the class interval $135 \leq h < 140$ will include all heights between 135cm and 140cm but not 140cm.

TOP TIP 2

$135 \leq h$ means that the height can be equal to 135cm.

KEY FACT 1

Grouped frequency diagrams are similar to bar charts except:

• There are no gaps between the bars.

• The data must be grouped into equal class intervals if the height of the bar is used to represent the frequency.

Question: Let's now draw a frequency diagram for the heights of the 20 students.

1 Decide on the scale for each axis.

The axes do not need to start at zero. The vertical axis is the frequency from 0 to 5. The horizontal axis goes from 120cm to 150cm.

2 Draw the axes on square or graph paper.

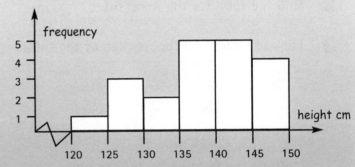

Notice the x axis does not start at zero so we use a jagged line.

3 Fill in the bars on the frequency diagram.

The numbers are the boundaries of the class intervals.

4 Check that there are no gaps between the bars.

No gaps between the bars.

5 Check that the axes are labelled.

Label both the horizontal and vertical axes.

Practice Questions

1) Draw a frequency diagram for the information given in this frequency table.

2) How many students had a weight of less than 60kg?

Weight (kg)	Frequency
$40 \leq kg < 50$	5
$50 \leq kg < 60$	7
$60 \leq kg < 70$	6
$70 \leq kg < 80$	2

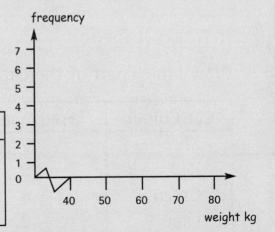

Constructing pie charts

For Level 6 you should be able to draw pie charts.

Question: The favourite subjects of 24 students are as follows:

Subject	Art	Maths	English	PE
Frequency	6	10	3	5

Draw a pie chart of this information.

1 Read the question then read it again.

2 Find the total for the items listed.

3 For each item find the fraction of the total.

A pie chart is a circle split up into sections.

In this case we know there are 24 students.

Subject	Frequency	Calculation	Angle
Art	6	$\frac{6}{24} \times 360°$	90°
Maths	10	$\frac{10}{24} \times 360°$	150°
English	3	$\frac{3}{24} \times 360°$	45°
PE	5	$\frac{5}{24} \times 360°$	75°

4 Multiply the fraction by 360° to find the angle.

5 Draw the pie chart accurately.

6 Measure the angles again just to check.

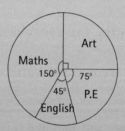

7 Label the sectors of the circle with the angle and category.

Label the angles and write the subjects in the appropriate sector.

Practice Question

1) Draw a pie chart of the data below.

Car Colour	Frequency
Blue	2
Red	9
Green	4
Lilac	3

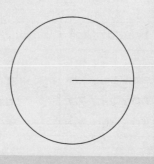

TOP TIP

Pie chart angles must be accurate to within 2°.

The probability that an event will not happen

KEY FACT 1
Probability of an event happening is:

$$P\ (event)\ =\ \frac{\text{Number of ways an event can happen}}{\text{Total number of outcomes}}$$

KEY FACT 2
All probabilities lie between 0 and 1.

KEY FACT 3
The total probability of all the mutually exclusive events of an experiment is 1.
From this we can say:

P (event will not happen) = 1 − P (event will happen).

Question: The probability that it snows today is $\frac{2}{13}$

What is the probability that it does not snow today?

---

1 Read the question then read it again.

2 All probabilities add up to 1.

3 Calculate the answer.

4 Check the answer.

5 If the answer is correct, write it in the box. If not go back to step 3.

Find the probability it does not snow.

P (does not snow) = 1 − P (will snow)

P (does not snow) = $1-\frac{2}{13}$

P (does not snow) = $\frac{11}{13}$

We can check by adding the two probabilities together: $\frac{11}{13}+\frac{2}{13}=1$

Practice Questions

1) The probability that I will win a tennis match is 0.62. What is the probability that I do not win the tennis match?

2) The probability that Jack is late to school on any given day is $\frac{2}{15}$. What is the probability that he will not be late for school?

Possible outcomes for combined events

For Level 6 you should know how to use lists, diagrams and tables to identify the outcomes of two events.

Sample space diagrams are useful when showing the outcomes of combined events. Let's look at this question.

Question: The spinner and a fair dice are thrown together and their scores are multiplied.

a) **Draw a sample space diagram**

b) **Work out the probability of a score of**

(i) 6 ☐

(ii) 12 ☐

---

1 (Read the question then read it again.)

I need to explore all possible outcomes.

2 (Draw the sample space diagram to show the possible outcomes.)

		Dice					
		1	2	3	4	5	6
	1	1	2	3	4	5	6
Spinner	2	2	4	6	8	10	12
	2	2	4	6	8	10	12
	3	3	6	9	12	15	18

3 on the spinner, 2 on the dice. 2 x 3 = 6

3 (Work out the number of outcomes.)

4 x 6 = 24 outcomes

4 (Answer the probability questions.)

(i) P (6) = $\frac{4}{24}$ = $\frac{1}{6}$

(ii) P (12) = $\frac{3}{24}$ = $\frac{1}{8}$

5 (Do the answers look sensible? Cancel the fractions down if possible. Write the answer in the box.)

It sometimes helps to put a ring or square around the numbers you need.

Tree diagrams are also another useful way when showing the outcomes of combined events. Probabilities always add up to 1.

Question: Two fair coins are thrown together. Draw a tree diagram to show the possible outcomes.
Work out the probability of:
   a) two heads
   b) a head and a tail

1 (Read the question then read it again.)

2 (Draw the tree diagram to show the outcomes.)

A tree diagram needs to be drawn.

Coin 1	Coin 2	Outcome

$\frac{1}{2}$ Head

$\frac{1}{2}$ Head $\frac{1}{2}$ Head   HH

$\frac{1}{2}$ Tail   HT

$\frac{1}{2}$ Tail

$\frac{1}{2}$ Head   TH

$\frac{1}{2}$ Tail   TT

3 (Check the branches add up to 1)

$\frac{1}{2} + \frac{1}{2} = 1$

4 (Calculate the answers to the probability questions.)

(i) P (head and head) $= \frac{1}{2} \times \frac{1}{2} = \frac{1}{4}$

(ii) P (a head and a tail)

P (H,T) $= \frac{1}{2} \times \frac{1}{2} = \frac{1}{4}$ ⎤
                              $\frac{1}{4} + \frac{1}{4} = \frac{1}{2}$

P (T,H) $= \frac{1}{2} \times \frac{1}{2} = \frac{1}{4}$ ⎦

5 (Does the answer look sensible? If so, write the answer in the box.)

Since there are two alternatives we add the probabilities together.

KEY FACT

Probabilities are written on the branches of the tree diagram and multiplied to obtain the final probabilities.

TOP TIP

When there are different alternatives, you add the probabilities together.

Scatter diagrams

For Level 6 you need to be able to draw scatter diagrams and understand correlation.

For Level 7 you need to be able to draw a line of best fit on a scatter diagram.

KEY FACT 1

A scatter diagram is used to show two sets of data at the same time.

It is used to show the connection (**correlation**) between two sets of data.

KEY FACT 2

There are three types of correlation:

Positive Correlation	**Negative Correlation**	**Zero Correlation**
This is when as one value increases so does the other	The is when as one value increases the other decreases	This is when there is no correlation between the values

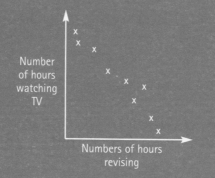

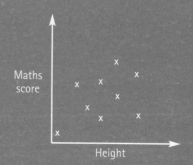

KEY FACT 3

'A line of best fit' is a line which best fits the data. It goes in the same direction as the data and has roughly the same number of points above the line as below it.

TOP TIP 1

Plot the points carefully, tick off the points when they are plotted.

TOP TIP 2

Check that you understand the scale on the axes before starting.

Question: a) Draw a scatter diagram of the following data.

Maths Paper 1	5	7	11	13	14	15	20	21	23	24	26	28	31	31	33	36	37	40
Maths Paper 2	6	9	12	10	14	17	19	23	21	23	26	29	31	33	34	36	37	37

b) Draw a line of best fit.

c) If a student scores 27 on Maths Paper 1, what is their approximate score on Paper 2?

1 (Read the question then read it again.)

2 (Work out the range of the values for each axes.)

range for Paper 1   5 – 40 = 35
range for Paper 2   6 – 37 = 31

3 (Draw the axes and label on graph paper.)

Axes will both be 0 to 40

4 (Plot the points carefully.)

This shows the completed scatter diagram.

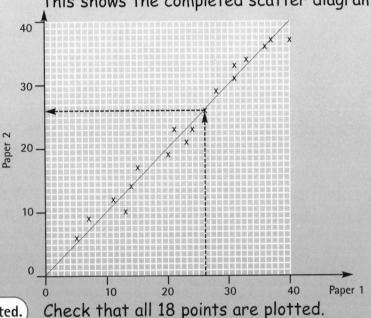

5 (Check that all the points have been plotted.)

Check that all 18 points are plotted.

6 (Draw on the line of Best fit.)

This must be in the direction of the data and does not need to go through (0, 0).

7 (Use the line of Best fit to estimate the answer to part c).)

Using the line of best fit, a score of 27 is estimated for Maths Paper 2.

Practice Questions

Decide for each of these pairs of variables whether they have a positive, negative or zero correlation.

a) Air temperature and distance up a mountain ☐

b) Number of scarves sold and the temperature ☐

c) Height and weight of children ☐

d) Maths score in a test and weight ☐

Averages of grouped data

When data is collected using a grouped frequency table the mean cannot be calculated exactly since all the individual data is not known. The mean can be estimated by finding the midpoint value.

KEY FACT

If x is the midpoint value: mean = $\dfrac{\text{sum of the frequency x midpoint}}{\text{sum of the frequency}}$

in other words: $x = \dfrac{\sum fx}{\sum f}$ $\sum$ = sum of
x = mean

Question: The grouped frequency table shows the weights (w) in kilograms of some students. Find an estimate for the mean weight of the students. Mean weight = ☐

Weight (w) kg	Frequency (f)
$30 \leq w < 40$	5
$40 \leq w < 50$	8
$50 \leq w < 60$	17
$60 \leq w < 70$	10

1 (Read the question then read it again.)   An estimate of the mean is needed.

2 (Think about the question.)   Find the midpoint of each class interval.

3 (Make a new table.)   Add in two extra columns.

Weight (w) kg	Frequency (f)	Midpoint (x)	$(f) \times (x)$
$30 \leq w < 40$	5	35	175
$40 \leq w < 50$	8	45	360
$50 \leq w < 60$	17	55	935
$60 \leq w < 70$	10	65	650

4 Study the numbers

You know the estimate for the mean weight is less than 70kg and more than 30kg.

5 Calculate your answer.

$$\frac{\sum fx}{\sum f} = \frac{175 + 360 + 935 + 650}{5 + 8 + 17 + 10}$$

$$= \frac{2120}{40}$$

$$x = 53$$

6 Add in the unit of measurement.

Estimated mean weight = 53kg

7 If the answer looks sensible, write it in the box.

If not, go back to step 3 and try again.

Finding the modal class

To find the modal class locate the class interval which has the highest frequency. In the example above, the highest frequency is 17 in the class interval $50 \le w < 60$

Modal class = $50 \le w < 60$

Finding the class interval that contains the median

This is a little more difficult.

Add up the frequency and add 1
$40 + 1 = 41$

Divide this by 2 $\quad \frac{41}{2} = 20.5$

This tells us that the median lies between the 20th and 21st data item.

Find the class interval with the 20th and 21st item.

Class interval containing the median is $50 \le w < 60$

Practice Questions

The grouped frequency table shows the time (t) in seconds it took for some swimmers to swim 100 metres.

Time (t)	Frequency (f)
$50 \le t < 60$	10
$60 \le t < 70$	15
$70 \le t < 80$	26
$80 \le t < 90$	14
$90 \le t < 100$	15

Using the information calculate:
a) An estimate of the mean time for the swimmers
b) The modal class
c) The class interval containing the median time

TOP TIP

Remember to add a column for the midpoint and the midpoint x frequency to show your working out.

Frequency polygons

KEY FACT
Frequency polygons are used to show the trend of some data. They are particularly useful to compare two or more sets of data.

Question: The grouped frequency table shows the time (t) in hours, spent per week on homework. The data shows the results for two Year 11 classes.

Class 11A

Time (t)	Frequency
$0 \le t < 2$	5
$2 \le t < 4$	8
$4 \le t < 6$	10
$6 \le t < 8$	7

Class 11B

Time (t)	Frequency
$2 \le t < 4$	12
$4 \le t < 6$	10
$6 \le t < 8$	5

a) Work out (i) the estimate of the mean time spent by each class (ii) the range
b) Draw a frequency polygon of the two distributions.
c) Which class obtained the better results? Explain why.

1 (Read the question then read it again.)

Group data to find the midpoint of the class intervals.

2 (Calculate an estimate of the mean.)

Class 11A mean = $\frac{128}{30}$ = 4.27hrs

Class 11B mean = $\frac{121}{27}$ = 4.48hrs

3 (Calculate the range.)

Class 11A range = 8 - 0 = 8
Class 11B range = 8 - 2 = 6

4 (Draw a frequency polygon for each class.)

Plot the midpoints of the class intervals:

5 (Compare the two frequency polygons.)

Class 11B spent slightly longer on their homework.

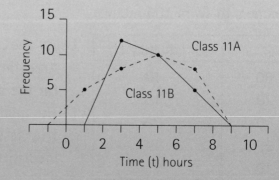

Designing questionnaires

For Level 7 you need to be able to design an appropriate survey sheet that takes bias into account.

Hypotheses

Data is usually collected to test an idea. Before the data is collected, you need to know what you hope to achieve. The statement that you want to test is called a hypothesis.

Examples of hypotheses are: 'Boys do better in history than girls.'
or '80% of cars are silver.'

Questionnaires

A questionnaire is used to test a hypothesis. The questions that you ask should help you to come to a decision about the hypothesis. When designing a questionnaire you need to remember the following key points.

KEY FACTS

- All questions should be relevant
- Do not write too many entries
- Questions should be easy to understand, requiring only one answer
- Avoid vague or misleading questions
- Provide alternative answers where possible, for example:

  Which colour is your favourite? Please tick one.

  Red ☐   Yellow ☐   Green ☐   Other ☐
- Avoid bias in your questions. For example, 'Do you agree that the swimming pool should be open on a Sunday morning?'
- Typed questionnaires look better

Relative frequency and probability

At Level 7 you need to understand that relative frequency is an estimate of probability and use this to compare the outcomes of experiments.

KEY FACT 1

When it is not possible to use equally likely outcomes you can only *estimate* probability.

An experiment is repeated to estimate the probability for an event. Each experiment is known as a *trial*.

KEY FACT 2

Relative frequency $= \dfrac{\text{the number of trials for the event}}{\text{total number of trials}}$

This only gives an estimate for the theoretical probability.

Question: A dice is thrown 300 times. The results are given in this table:

Score	1	2	3	4	5	6
Frequency	61	42	50	56	58	33

Use relative frequency to estimate the probability of getting a 4

1 (Read the question then read it again.)

Relative frequency is an estimate

2 (How many trials are there?)

There are 300 trials in this experiment

3 (Remember the formula for relative frequency.)

Relative frequency =
$\dfrac{\text{number of trials for event}}{\text{total number of trials}}$

4 (Calculate the relative frequency.)

Relative frequency $= \dfrac{56}{300} = \dfrac{14}{75}$

5 (Compare with theoretical probability.)

Theoretical probability $= \dfrac{1}{6}$

KEY FACT 3

The more trials conducted in an experiment, the closer the estimate will be to the theoretical probability.

Question: A spinner is spun 120 times. The results are given in this table:

Score	1	2	3	4
Frequency	60	21	30	9

Use relative frequency to estimate the probability of getting a 4. Decide if the spinner is biased.

1 Read the question then read it again.

Estimate the relative frequency

2 How many trials are there?

There are 120 trials in this experiment

3 Calculate the relative frequency.

Relative frequency = $\frac{9}{120}$

4 Compare with the theoretical probability.

Theoretical probability = $\frac{1}{4}$

The relative frequency of getting a 4 is much lower than expected.
It does appear that the spinner is biased.

Practice Questions

1) A coin is thrown 500 times.
The results are:

Heads	320
Tails	180

Use relative frequency to estimate the probability of getting a tail.

2) A dice is thrown 600 times.
The results are given in the table:

Score	1	2	3	4	5	6
Frequency	95	110	96	105	94	100

Use relative frequency to estimate the probability of getting a 5.

Tips and Techniques

Before a test

1. When you revise, try revising 'a little and often' rather than in long sessions.
2. Warm up by practising mental arithmatic with a friend. Give each other questions to answer.
3. Revise with a friend. You can encourage and learn from each other.
4. Get a good night's sleep the night before.
5. Be prepared – bring your own pens and pencils and wear a watch to check the time as you go.
6. Learn important formulae.

During a test

1. Don't rush the first few questions. These tend to be quite straightforward, so don't make any silly mistakes.
2. Make sure you READ THE QUESTION THEN READ IT AGAIN.
3. If you get stuck, don't linger on the same question – move on! You can come back to it later.
4. Check to see how many marks a question is worth. Have you 'earned' those marks with your answer?
5. Check your answers. You can use the inverse method or the rounding method. Does your answer look correct?
6. Be aware of the time. After 20 minutes, check to see how far you have got.
7. Try to leave a couple of minutes at the end to read through what you have written.
8. Always show your method. You may get a mark for showing you have gone through the correct procedure even if your answer is wrong.
9. Don't leave any question unanswered. In the two minutes you have left yourself at the end, make an educated guess at the questions you really couldn't do.

Answers

LEVEL 5 – THE TRICKY BITS

Page 7 – Multiplication and division
1) 18   2) 21.5   3) 31   4) 12834   5) 30573   6) 12

Page 9 – Simple formulae
1) £300   2) 5   3) £7
A = 8N - 10

Page 10 – Units of measure
1) 8 litres   2) 360 grams   3) 16 kilometres   4) 4.09 kilograms

Page 11 – Graphs
1) €24   2) €56   3) £25   4) £40

LEVEL 6 AND 7

Page 12 – Decimals
1) 2.06, 2.11, 2.3, 2.52
2) 3.07, 3.57, 3.7, 3.72
3) 2.09, 2.71, 3.602, 3.62, 3.621
4) 5.06, 5.12, 5.125, 5.27, 5.6

Page 13 – One quantity as a percentage of another
1) 62%   2) 27%   3) 40%   4) 44%

Page 14 – Adding and subtracting fractions
1) 1 4/15   2) 5/12   3) 29/45   4) 1 1/6   5) 1/4

Page 16 – Ratio
1) £16, £12   2) £48, £52   3) 1800g of flour
4) £1.87   5) £2.40   6) 420 pear trees

Page 17 – Finding the nth term of a linear sequence
1) $2n$ 2) $2n + 3$ 3) $4n - 1$ 4) $2n - 1$

Page 18 – Linear equations
1) $n = 4$ 2) $n = 3$ 3) $n = 7$ 4) $n = 3$
5) $n = 5$ 6) $n = 3$ 7) $n = -2$ 8) $n = -4$

Page 19 – Linear equations
1) $n = 4$ 2) $n = 4$ 3) $n = 5$ 4) $n = 2$
5) $n = 9$ 6) $n = 2/3$ 7) $n = 7.5$ 8) $n = 1$

Page 20 – Drawing linear graphs

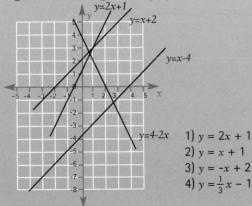

1) $y = 2x + 1$
2) $y = x + 1$
3) $y = -x + 2$
4) $y = \frac{1}{3}x - 1$

Page 21 – Drawing linear graphs
1) $y = x + 1$ 2) $y = 2 - x$ 3) $y = \frac{1}{3}x - 1$

Page 22 – Significant figures and estimating
1) $3 \times 5 = 15$ 2) $60^2 = 3600$
3) $\dfrac{300 \times 40}{4} = \dfrac{12000}{4} = 3000$
4) $(70 \times 10)^2 = (700)^2 = 490000$

Page 23 – Multiplying and dividing by numbers between 0 and 1
1) 8.7   2) 220   3) 0.084   4) 11000
5) 1.24   6) 7000   7) 1.41   8) 120000

Page 25 – Proportional changes
1) £28   2) £43.24   3) £121305.60   4) £61.11

Page 26 – The efficient use of a calculator
1) 5.97   2) 2.88   3) 32.25

Page 27 – Finding the nth term of a quadratic sequence
1) n^2 2) $2n^2 + 3$ 3) $2n^2 - 3$ 4) $n^2 - 4$

Page 28 – Multiplying out brackets
1) $2x + 2$ 2) $3x - 6$ 3) $-4x + 16$ 4) $6 + x - x^2$
5) $x^2 - 9x + 20$ 6) $x^2 - 8x + 12$ 7) $x^2 - y^2$

Page 29 – Solving inequalities
1) $x < 5$ 2) $x \le 3$ 3) $x \le 5$ 4) $x \ge 3$ 5) $x > -2.5$
6) $x < 3$ 7) $x \ge -3$ 8) $x \ge 1$ 9) $x \ge -2$ 10) $x \ge 1$

Page 31 – Simultaneous equations
1) $x = 2, y = 2$ 2) $x = 1, y = 2$ 3) $x = 5, y = 1$

Page 32 – 2-D Representations of 3-D objects

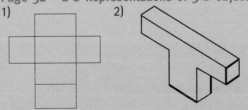

Page 35 – Intersecting lines and parallel lines
1) a = 82° vertically opposite   b = 98° supplementary
   c = 98° corresponding
2) e = 65° alternate   f = 65° vertically opposite
   g = 115° supplementary

Page 36 – Logo and transformations

Page 38 – The circle
1) Circumference = 75.36cm   Area = 452.16cm²
2) Circumference = 35.17cm   Area = 98.47cm²
3) Circumference = 62.8cm   Area = 314cm²

Page 39 – Volumes of cubes and cuboids
1) Volume = 12.167cm³   2) 49.14cm³

Page 43 – Pythagoras' theorem
1) 9.4cm   2) 6.6cm   3) 12.7cm   4) 394.5km

Page 44 – Accuracy of measurement
1) $61.5 \leq d < 62.5$ 2) $12.25 \leq l < 12.35$
3) $16.75 \leq t < 16.85$

Page 45 – Compound measures
1) 30km   2) 3.125g/cm³   3) 6 hours 40 minutes

Page 47 - Areas of compound shapes and volumes of prisms
a) 324cm³   b) 423.9cm³

Page 49 – Frequency diagrams for continuous data
(1)

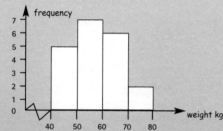

(2) 12 students

Page 50 – Constructing pie charts

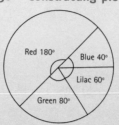

Page 51 – The probability that an event will not happen
1) 0.38   2) $\frac{13}{15}$

Page 55 – Scatter diagrams
(a) Negative   (b) Negative   (c) Positive   (d) Zero

Page 57 – Averages of grouped data
(a) $= \frac{6090}{80} = 76.125$ seconds

(b) $70 \leq t < 80$ (c) $70 \leq t < 80$

Page 61 - Relative frequency and probability
1. $\frac{180}{500} = \frac{9}{25}$ 2. $\frac{94}{600} = \frac{47}{300}$

Rising Stars UK Ltd, 76 Farnaby Road, Bromley BR1 4BH
www.risingstars-uk.com

Every effort has been made to trace copyright holders and obtain their permission for the use of copyright materials. The authors and publisher will gladly receive information enabling them to rectify any error or omission in subsequent editions.

All facts are correct at time of going to press.

Published 2004
Text, design and layout © Rising Stars UK Ltd.

Editorial: Steph Preston/Louise Moore
Design: Button Group plc
Illustrations: Burville-Riley, Button Design plc and Oxford Illustrators
Cover photo: Getty Images
Cover Design: Burville-Riley

All rights reserved. No part of this publication may be reproduced, stored in a retrieval system, or transmitted, in any form by any means, electronic, mechanical, photocopying, recording or otherwise, without the prior permission of Rising Stars.

British Library Cataloguing in Publication Data.
A CIP record for this book is available from the British Library.

ISBN: 1-904591-33-7

Printed by Wyndeham Gait, Grimsby, UK